A LIFETIME IN STEEL

A pictorial history of iron and steelmaking in Rotherham

Rotherham Metropolitan Borough Council
Department of Libraries, Museum and Arts
1987

Front Cover:
Thrybergh Bar Mill - Cooling Beds

Back Cover:
THE MUNITIONS GIRLS - Forging 4.5 shells at Kilnhurst Steelworks by Stanhope Forbes, R.A. (1857-1947)

The painting was commissioned from the artist by George Baker in 1918. In 1983 it was added to the Science Museum collection, purchased with aid of a grant made by the National Heritage Memorial Fund.

The munitions girls known to be in the painting are Mrs. Newby, Mrs. Hart, Mrs. Muscroft, Mrs. Robinson, Mrs. Whiteley, Mrs. Tooley; all daughters of local workers in Swinton or Kilnhurst. The exceptions are the two foreground figures who were painted from models in Forbes' studio.

The picture caused an uproar when it was exhibited at the Royal Academy from a public who were shocked at the sight of women in factory dress and making weapons. Forbes writing a letter to Mrs. George Baker at the beginning of the Second World War recalled a different view:-"It was indeed an unforgettable sight to see those fine women carrying on their work so splendidly and the opportunity which Mr. Baker gave me to record this wonderful service is one for which I can never be sufficiently grateful".

First published in 1987 by Metropolitan Borough of Rotherham, Department of Libraries, Museum and Arts, Central Library and Arts Centre, Walker Place, Rotherham, S65 1JH.

ISBN 0 903666 32 4

Designed by Information and Publicity Service, Rotherham Metropolitan Borough Council

Printed by Joseph Ward & Co., Dewsbury

Contents

ACKNOWLEDGEMENTS

We would like to thank Messrs. R. Cutts, P. Hayden and H. Hudd for their reminiscences and the following who have generously loaned us photographs for inclusion in the book (as well as may other people who loaned us photographs which we were unfortunately unable to include):-

Mr. R. Barnes
British Steel Corporation
Mr. D. Creswell
Mr. J. Durham
Mr. R. Dyal
Miss M. Haigh
Mrs. C. Harvey
Mr. C. B. Heap
Mr. E. Hoyle
Mrs. K. Newbould
Mrs. J. Palmer
The Science Museum
Sheffield Record Office
Mr. J. Swinscoe
United Engineering Steels Limited

This book is published to coincide with an exhibition mounted in the Art Gallery in the Brian O'Malley Central Library and Arts Centre, Rotherham in December, 1987 and January, 1988. We would also like to thank everyone who has assisted with, or lent materials for, the exhibition and, in particular, the following for their generous sponsorship:-

The Melchett Trust
The Iron and Steel Trades Confederation
Brinsworth Strip Mill

Introduction

by his worship the Mayor of Rotherham, Councillor K. E. Billington

The Iron and Steel Industry of Rotherham has been an integral part of the life of the town and of thousands of its citizens over the years.

The skyline has been dominated by its blast furnaces, melting shop chimneys and vast rolling mill buildings, and its products have been exported around the world.

Products such as cannons, iron castings, stove grates, even bridges were manufactured in the early days. Two World Wars saw the town gearing up to armament production; and bars, billets, steel strip, railway wheels and axles, forgings of all descriptions—the list goes on and on—have since poured from the works.

Many of the firms, some now gone, are still household names—Midland Iron and Steel Co., Baker Bessemer, Don Forge, Steel Peech and Tozer, and Park Gate Iron and Steel Co. (the last two known colloquially as Steelo's and Parkgate Forge respectively).

The town is still an important centre for steel production using the most up-to-date technology.

This is not a definitive history of the industry, it would take volumes to cover that. Rather it is hoped that this book will give a flavour of what it was, and is, like to work in the industry—the works themselves, the machinery, social gatherings and sports activities. It is dedicated to the many thousand of men and women who worked in the industry, and those that still do, from the early times up to the present day.

MAP

1. Templeborough Melting Shop)
2. Billet and Bar Mills)
3. Disc and Tyre Mills)
4. 10 in. and 14 in. Mill) Steel, Peech and Tozer
5. Rotherham Melting Shop)
6. Brinsworth Strip Mill)
7. Templeborough Rolling Mills
8. Rother Iron Works (Owen and Dyson)
9. South Yorkshire Hoop Iron Works
10. Ickles Forge (Allot Brothers and Leigh)
11. Holmes Blast Furnace (Parkgate Iron and Steel Co. Ltd.)
12. Peter Stubbs Ltd.
13. J. J. Habershon and Sons Ltd.
14. Rotherham Wagon Works (Harrison and Camm Ltd.)
15. Robert Jenkins and Co. Ltd.
16. Ferham Works (J. and R. Corker)
17. Clough Works (W.H. Micklethwaite and Co. Ltd.)
18. Midland Iron Co. Ltd.
19. Midland Steel Works, later Don Steel Works
20. Millmoor Works (William Heaton and Co. Ltd.)
21. Burton Weir Works (George Wright (Rotherham) Ltd.)
22. Brinsworth Iron andWheel Works (John Baker and Bessemer Ltd.)
23. Wheathill Foundry (Don Forge and Engineering Co.)
24. Westgate Foundry (George Cawood and Son Ltd.)
25. Baths Foundry (Rotherham Steel Strip Co. Ltd.)
26. Rotherham Foundry (Yates, Haywood and Co.)
27. Rotherham Forge and Rolling Mills Ltd.
28. Cupola Works (Steel)
29. Masbrough Works (Skelton, Corbitt and Co.)
30. Effingham Works (Yates, Haywood and Co.)
31. Phoenix Forge (Owen's Patent Wheel, Tyre and Axle Co.)
32. Don Spring Works (E. Cottam & Co. Ltd.)
33. Northfield Works (Steel)
34. Park Gate Steel Works (William Oxley and Co. Ltd.)
35. Park Gate Iron and Steel Co. Ltd.
36. Roundwood Rolling Mill (Park Gate Iron and Steel Co. Ltd.)
37. Aldwarke Works (Park Gate Iron and Steel Co. Ltd.)
38. Thrybergh Bar Mill (B.S.C.)

Not on the map:

39. Kilnhurst Works (John Baker and Bessemer Ltd.)
40. Queen's Foundry, Swinton (Hattersley Brothers Ltd.)
41. White Lee Iron Works, Swinton (Charles H. Verity Ltd.)

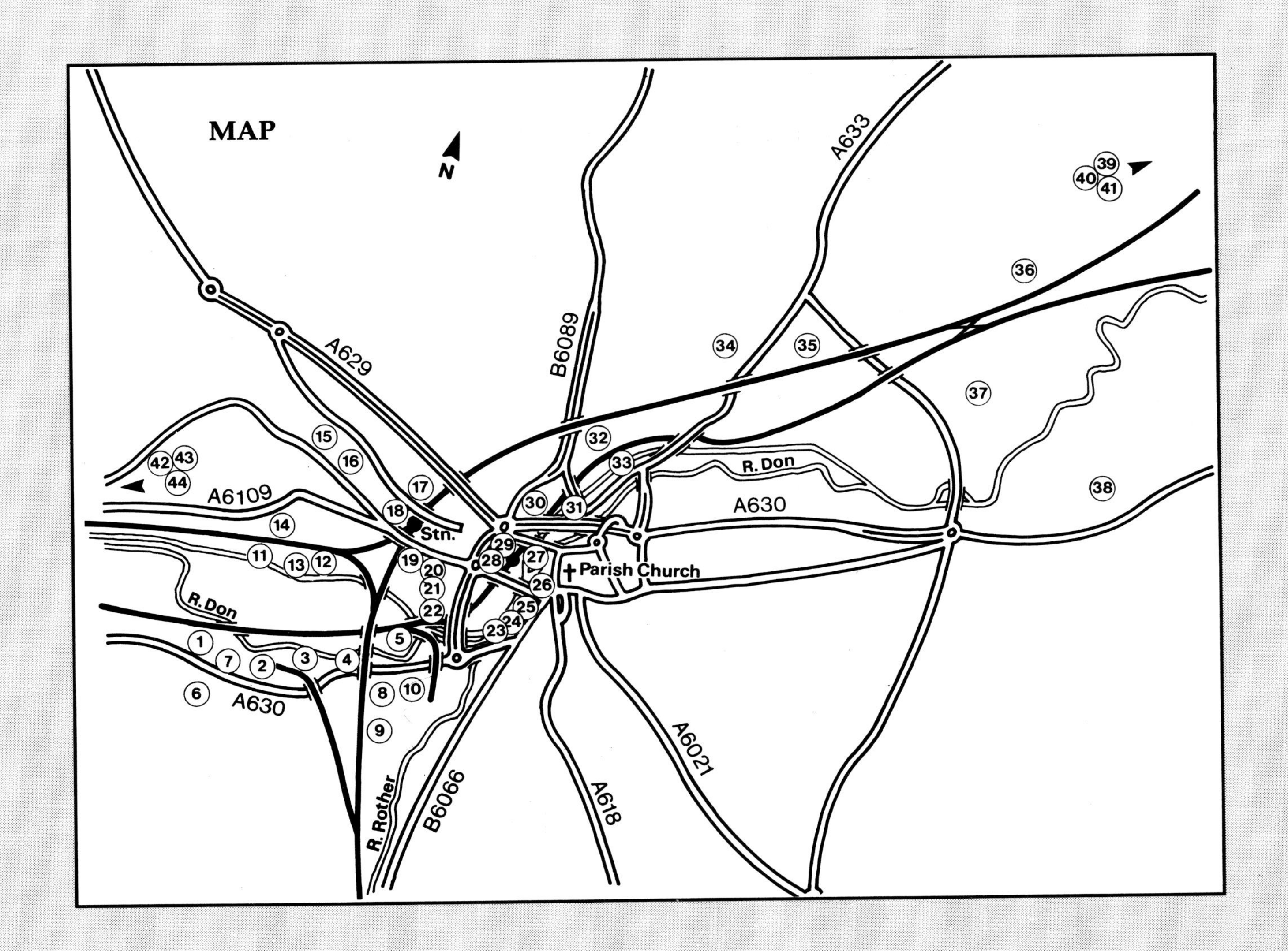
MAP
N
A629
B6089
A633
A6109
R. Don
A630
Stn.
Parish Church
R. Rother
B6066
A618
A6021
1
2
3
4
5
6
7
8
9
10
11
12
13
14
15
16
17
18
19
20
21
22
23
24
25
26
27
28
29
30
31
32
33
34
35
36
37
38
39
40
41
42
43
44

1 Memories

Steel workers labour in an industry which has always been known for its heavy physical work. They have a pride in doing "men's work" and are proud to be called steel workers.

The steelworks had a family-feel to them. "You had to have a relative there to get a job - I had - my Dad worked there", said one former steelworker. On the other hand since 15,000 or more were involved with steel "every family had somebody working at Steel Peech and Tozer". Not everybody got in that way however; "My Dad said, 'You're not going down the pit!' and the headmaster announced they were taking on lads at Don Forge so I went," was one man's version. "When we first started they gave us an induction and took us into the melting shop and it was frightening - I couldn't imagine the people working there, it looked like Hell" remembered a woman office worker.

"I started at 15 at Templeborough Melting shop", one man told us. "There were 14 open hearth furnaces at that time - they said it was the largest in the world - it was gigantic. You were just a little over 15 years old and you wondered what was happening".

Once employed, the usual problems of being the newest recruit would start. "When you were spare tube lad you went and got the snap and mashed for them all - you had to make sure everybody had their billy can full of tea". "If you made a mistake you got a little friendly tap, and if it was a bad mistake you got a reasonably hard tap". But the doler out of this treatment thinks it worked "Now the lads say 'You brought us up right though didn't you?' ". The tricks that men have played on young lads over the years were again trotted out "You'd be sent for a bucket of steam, or a left handed spanner, or a sky-hook". But this was all part of the vital start, getting accepted on to a team. "You worked your way through the team, whatever job came up you looked for the next move up. You had to be accepted by the team - once you were accepted you worked as a team and you knew you were going to earn some good money".

"You decided as a youngster which line you would take, you could either go on to the mill crew that looked after the roughing mills and finishing stands, or the control team that controlled rolls (you moved up to the cogging mill pulpit). The cogger was the best paid, the roller was the best paid on the mill crew and there was another line you could go on - furnacing. They'd got 48 soaking pits when I started at Templeborough - first hand heater, he was top job on that and those three, first hand heater, roller and cogger, they were gods" - and they usually held top positions in the Unions as well. The key

Fettling open hearth furnace at Templeborough in 1961. Arthur Garrison is furnaceman.

position of these 'gods' is obvious. The pay was good, the team was yours and so was a heavy responsibility.

"They'd learned the trade through experience" in those pre-computerised days "the first hand would get a sample out and say 'that's ready' and they'd tap". The team, led by the first hand was all important. Men would turn down promotion to stay on a good team, the basic money might be better, but the final wage depended on production, and that depended on the team.

"There were three shifts and it was like three teams competing against each other" a memory of Steel Peech and Tozer borne out by other memories. Shifts would organise fishing outings, trips to cricket matches, cricket teams and even all sign on together when short time was the order of the day.

Much of the tightness of the team stemmed from the knowledge that the men were juggling with scalding hot metal and fierce machinery. Although disasters did not overtake a complete shift as they did in the coal fields, danger was ever present. "Not long after I started a slag pot exploded. Slag finished on the other side of the road and set a field alight. It killed two people". "A wheelwright's mate was holding a big spanner, and the wheelwright was using a 16-lb hammer on it. He missed and hit the labourer. The labourer took his glove off and said 'How much do you get for losing a finger', that was the first comment he made - and he's lost his finger".

For one set of men the loss of a finger would be mild. Trying to get the diamond shaped ingots to feed in the right way round, sharp end first, was the under-roller's job. "They had a big fork and have to get hold of the ingot and pull it over and many a time it would slip and they'd trap their hands, and most under-rollers had just two fingers missing because of this, and these were just accepted, these accidents, when I was young".

You grew used to the conditions. One man tells the story of his visit to Rotherham's other industry - coal. "I went down Silverwood pit and they'd just finished cutting a cross-face and the roof was just settling on to the props and God! I was scared to death, and there was a miner there and he said 'Where are you from then?' and I said 'I'm from Steelos' and he said 'I wouldn't work there. It's too bloody dangerous in the steel works'. It's what you're used to isn't it?"

The Steel industry, like other hot, dirty industries, has a reputation for heavy drinking, but old hands thought this was exaggerated, at least at work. "It was a little too serious for that" claimed a worker from Don Forge, "you couldn't work on the hammer if you'd had some pop". At the larger Steel Peech and Tozer however, "the hot departments negotiated a beer note in the summer, and they allowed them out for half an hour refreshments in the Temple Hotel - it was abused at times but mostly they'd be back after half an hour. But (with a slight twinkle in the eye) that continued in the winter as well".

If the heavy drinking is an exaggerated myth, stories of how the men used the ample heat at their disposal are not. On one shift someone "used to bring kippers on a Friday night and warm them up near the rolls that were going past. But this lad would put them under the rolls and you'd get this terrible stench of kippers for the rest of the shift".

"You'd fill your cans up and boil them on a forging that was going cold. Or you'd clean up the top of an anvil, put some bread on, put a cutter into the fire to get warm, come back, give it a knock and then waft it across the top of the bread. It was quicker than making toast at home".

Both large and small managed to introduce some irregularity into their programmes "We had the finest set of mechanics and welders and everything in England - nobody paid a bill for having his car mended. Being a grinder I'd grind scissors, shears, mowers, for half a crown or the cost of a pint when there was nobody knocking about".

Because the steel works were so embedded in the life of the town a host of local memories are of events connected with the works, none more so than the Soaker's Christmas Club and Christmas Party held at Ickles, where all your children got a slap-up meal and a present and a conjurer, while the adults danced, drank and enjoyed themselves in the 500 Room.

Of course, there were conflicts, one shop steward had his boss frequently shouting "I run this firm not you!" but when the same shop steward got involved in Health and Safety legislation and went round one Saturday and threw away all the work force's favourite tools on the grounds that they were dangerous he found that they could get equally irate. In the end though what stands out is that everyone was in it together, all Rotherham was involved in steel and once you had started, once on your team, it seemed that town and worker alike looked forward to a lifetime in steel.

2 The companies

In the centuries before the Industrial Revolution, the siting of heavy industry, such as iron making, depended on the easy availability of raw materials. The presence of shallow beds of iron ore and plentiful woodland to provide charcoal made it inevitable that an iron industry would develop in South Yorkshire at an early date. The archaelogical evidence for prehistoric iron-working in the Rotherham area is non-existent, although iron slag has been found at Wincobank and at a settlement site at Clifton near Conisborough. The hurried excavations of the Roman fort at Templeborough in 1916-17 revealed extensive evidence of iron working.

The earliest documentary evidence for the industry in Rotherham does not occur until 1161 when Richard de Busli, lord of the manor of Kimberworth, granted Kirkstead Abbey the right to mine and smelt iron at Kimberworth. Little surface evidence remains of the monastic ironworks at Kirkstead Abbey Grange, largely because the extensive slagheaps were resmelted in the late 18th century. The industry remained important throughout the medieval era. The poll tax returns for 1391 reveal that Kimberworth and Greasborough had more smithies per head than any other place in the West Riding. At that period iron was produced in bloomeries, shallow furnaces in which the iron was heated by charcoal. Forced draft was provided by bellows which were initially hand powered but were later harnessed to water power. The resulting spongy mass of iron and slag was then hammered to drive out impurities before being cut into bars. The increasing use of water power led to a growth of the industry in Sheffield, where a good head of water was easily attained, with a corresponding decline in Rotherham. When Leland visited Rotherham c.1535 he reported a thriving iron industry but in 1586 William Camden stated the industry in Rotherham had sadly declined and was now "quite lost".

The industry was not, however, completely dead. The old bloomeries were being replaced by charcoal blast furnaces. These attained temperatures sufficient to produce molten iron that could be cast into finished articles or into pigs for subsequent use elsewhere. In 1589 the Earl of Shrewsbury had two blast furnaces in this area, one at Wadsley and the other, Jordan Furnace, on the river Don at Kimberworth. The iron produced by these furnaces was refined at Attercliffe Forge. In 1666 the forges at Rotherham, Wardsend and Attercliffe and the blast-furnace at Chapeltown were leased to Lionel Copley for £200 a year. Under the lease Copley was to convert Rotherham Forge into a slitting mill to produce bar iron for the nail making industry. Some idea of the vast quantities of charcoal consumed in iron making can be obtained from this lease which gave Copley the right to cut 1500 cords of wood

(21,333 cubic yards) each year for charcoal.

After Copley's death in 1675, the Rotherham area works became part of a larger combine controlled by a series of partnerships dominated by the Spencer family of Cannon Hall. At one time, the partners controlled almost the whole of the iron industry from North Derbyshire to Mid-Lancashire. The combine included forges at Kilnhurst, Thrybergh and Roche. By the 1740s the local iron ore was becoming difficult to mine and wholesale destruction of the woodland had made charcoal difficult to obtain. The local iron industry began to decline but was saved by Abraham Darby's development of the smelting of iron with coke at Coalbrookdale. In 1743 the Don Navigation reached Rotherham, offering the possibility of easier transport to a wider market. These new opportunities were exploited by the Walker family.

Jonathan, Samuel and Aaron Walker were the sons of Joseph Walker of Grenoside, who combined farming with nail making. After Joseph's death in 1729, the brothers continued the family enterprises, expanding to include iron founding. By the mid 1740s they had discovered the secret of Benjamin Huntsman's crucible steel process and had established a steel casting business at Grenoside. In 1746 the decision was made to move to Masbrough, the main attraction being the Don Navigation. Initially a charcoal furnace was built, followed in 1767 by a coke furnace. By this time they had expanded by leasing the Earl of Effingham's Holmes Estate, including the existing rolling and slitting mills. While they continued to produce steel, their main business became the smelting, rolling and casting of iron. By 1800 the works was the largest in the North of England and, in addition to Masbrough, included forges at Rotherham, Thrybergh and Conisbrough. The Walker's success was based on the production of cannon, initially for the War of American Independence and later for the Napoleonic Wars, coupled with other large-scale castings, such as those of the Southwark Bridge. The company remained profitable after 1815 but the loss of the market for cannon, coupled with gloomy predictions about the future of the iron trade, led the partners in 1820 to resolve to wind up their business.

The closure of the Walkers' business could have been an economic disaster for Rotherham. In fact, most of the Walkers' works continued in production under new owners who were often former Walker employees. James Yates was a relative of the Walkers and had been manager of their Holmes Foundry. In 1823 he went into partnership with Charles Sandford to take over the Walkers' foundry interests. They also acquired the Phoenix Works on Greasborough Road and in 1833 took over Rotherham Foundry at Domine Well. The partners separated in 1838. Charles Sandford concentrated on the forging side of the business at Phoenix Works in partnership with William Owen. This business later became Owen's Patent Wheel, Tire and Axle Co. Ltd. James Yates retained the foundry work. Needing more room, he took over the former Beatson's earthenware pottery and adjacent Masbrough Flax Mill, renaming the complex the Effingham Works. George Haywood and George Drabble were taken into partnership in 1846, the business being renamed Yates, Haywood and Co. A new factory, also called Effingham Works, was erected on Tenter Green in 1852-56. Yates, Haywood and Co. produced a wide range of stoves, fire-places, kitchen ranges and general castings. The company went into voluntary liquidation in 1908 and was bought in 1911 by O'Brien, Thomas and Co. of London but continued to trade under the old name. It became an independent company again in 1952 but its traditional market was being eroded by the growth of gas, oil and electricity for heating and cooking. Takeover by William Heatons Holdings Ltd. in 1967 was followed by complete closure in 1970. Other prominent firms in the stove-grate industry in Rotherham included W.H. Micklethwait and Co. Ltd. of Clough Works, George Wright (Rotherham) Ltd. of Burton Weir Works, Skelton, Corbitt and Co. of Sheffield Grate Works (all at Masbrough) and Hattersley Bros. Ltd. of Swinton.

Matthew Habershon, another ex-employee, took over the Walkers' tin-plate works at Holmes, comverting it into a rolling mill. The company, incorporated in 1920 as J. J. Habershon and Son Ltd., later specialised in rolling steel strip, initially for such mundane products as pen nibs and corset springs but more recently for the aircraft industry. The company, by then part of the G.K.N. group, closed in 1981.

The Warrington toolmaking company of Peter Stubs chose Masbrough as a base to supply high-grade steel. In 1829 part of the former Walker works at the Holmes were acquired and steel production started. These premises became too small and Stubs purchased the site of Holmes Hall where an imposing new steelworks was erected in 1842. Stubs ceased to use the site in 1958 and the works were sold to J. J. Habershon and Sons Ltd. whose rolling mills adjoined the site. The works were completely demolished in 1968-69.

In the present century the two largest iron and steel works in the Rotherham area were undoubtedly Park Gate Iron and Steel Co. Ltd. and Steel, Peech and Tozer Ltd. The works at Parkgate date back to 1823 and passed through several hands until Scholefield, Geach and Beale entered into partnership in 1845. The first blast furnace on the site had been erected in 1839 on the west side of Broad Street. The early prosperity of the company was based on the rolling of rails for the expanding railway network. In 1849 land on the east side of Broad Street was purchased to allow for expansion and the company became the first to produce rolled armour plate for the Royal Navy. Two additional blast furnaces were erected in 1871 to be replaced by two modern furnaces in 1905. The company also operated the Holmes blast furnaces from 1854 until 1920. Following the nationalisation of 1951-53, the company was sold to Tube Investments Ltd. in 1956. A new rolling mill complex had been erected at Roundwood in 1950-53. The new owners invested in further expansion with the construction of the country's first Kaldo steel plant at Aldwarke, opened in 1964. Both Roundwood and Aldwarke remain in use, although the Kaldo furnaces were replaced with electric arc furnaces in 1974. The original Park Gate Works were demolished, following the felling of the last blast-furnace in 1976.

Steel, Peech and Tozer Ltd. was the creation of Henry Steel and William Peech, who retired from a successful book-making business in Sheffield, seeking a new challenge.In 1875 they took over the bankrupt Phoenix Bessemer Steel Co. works at Ickles and expanded rapidly. With the completion of the Templeborough Melting Shop in 1917, the works stretched for over a mile along the Sheffield road. In 1918 Steel, Peech and Tozer Ltd. joined with Samuel Fox and Co. Ltd. of Stocksbridge, Workington Iron and Steel Co. Ltd., Rother Vale Collieries, Frodingham Iron and Steel Co. Ltd. and Appleby Iron and Steel Co. Ltd. to form the United Steel Companies Ltd. United Steel Cos. was the first steel company to be denationalised after the nationalisation of 1951-53. A poicy of updating and expansion was followed with the building of Brinsworth Strip Mill in 1955-58 and the conversion from open-hearth to electric arc furnaces in 1960-63. Owen and Dyson Ltd. at Ickles was slightly older than Steel, Peech and Tozer having been founded in 1873, and concentrated on the production of railway wheels and axles. Steel, Peech and Tozer Ltd. took a substantial shareholding in the company in 1907. Owen and Dyson became a wholly-owned subsidiary of S.P.T. in 1955, being completely absorbed in 1961.

The third largest company in the area was John Baker and Bessemer Ltd., founded by John Baker who had been manager of Owens Patent Wheel, Tire and Axle Co. He set up on his own account, assembling wheels and axles at Conisborough, moving to larger premises at the Brinsworth Iron and Wheels Works, New York, Masbrough in 1884. In 1903 it was decided that the company needed to control all stages of construction from steelmaking to final assembly and a new factory was built, on the site of a former steelworks, at Kilnhurst. The name was changed from John Baker and Co. (Rotherham) Ltd. to John Baker and Bessemer Ltd. in 1929, following the takeover of the bankrupt Henry Bessemer and Co. During both World Wars the company's production was almost entirely turned over to shell production. The Brinsworth works closed in the 1950s followed by the Kilnhurst works in 1964.

These are only some of the many companies that have made Rotherham, iron and steel centre of international importance and whose work is being continued by Rotherham Engineering Steels and B.S.C. Sadly there is no room to give other than a mention to the Midland Iron Co. Ltd. at Masbrough, Rotherham Forge and Rolling Mills Ltd., the Baths, Wheathill and Don Foundries in Westgate, Northfield Iron Works (famous for anchors) and William Oxley's Parkgate Steel Works.

WORKS OF THE PARKGATE IRON & STEEL Co LIMD. ROTHERHAM.

Above: This bird's eye view of Park Gate Iron and Steel Co. Ltd. dates from the 1880s. The original blast furnace can be seen at the left rear, adjacent to the Rotherham-Rawmarsh road. In 1871 two new furnaces were erected in the centre of the works. The inset, top right, shows the Holmes Blast Furnaces at Masbrough which were operated by the company until the 1920s.

Right: Taken in 1948, this aerial photograph shows that considerable development had taken place since the previous view. The three original blast furnaces were replaced c.1910 by a bank of new furnaces fronting Aldwarke Road. All these buildings have now been swept away. Aldwarke Main Colliery can be seen at the top right.

Above A panoramic view of Parkgate works in 1923, looking northwards from the Midland Railway embankment.

Right: An intrepid photographer scaled the roof of J. J. Habershon and Sons rolling mills at the Holmes to take this panoramic view in 1928. The company originated with Matthew Habershon who took over the Holmes Rolling Mills from his former employers, the Walkers. The chimney of one of the early furnaces can be seen at the right. The works, by then part of the GKN group, closed in 1981 and the site was cleared. The chimneys of Templeborough Melting Shop dominate the skyline.

The No. 9 Gate at Ickles was the main entrance to Steel, Peech and Tozer. All these buildings, which housed the typing pool, postroom, sales and other administrative departments have now gone.

The main Sheffield-Rotherham road ouside the Steel, Peech and Tozer offices and the works at Ickles was notorious for flooding. This photograph, taken in 1950, shows the conditions that drivers had to face. The roof of the main offices can be seen above the railway bridge. No. 9 Gate is just visible through the arch.

The blast furnaces come down during clearance of the site by the British Steel Corporation in 1976.

The blast furnaces at Parkgate seen from Lloyd Street, shortly before demolition. These were the only modern blast furnaces to be operated in South Yorkshire.

The imposing entrance to Peter Stubs steelworks at the Holmes, Masbrough. The cone of one of the six cementation furnaces can be seen through the arch. Designed by the Sheffield architect William Flockton, the works were erected in 1842 to supply high-grade steel to Peter Stubs's tool making factory at Warrington. After Stubs ceased to use the complex in 1958 it was taken over by J. J. Habershon and Sons Ltd. and finally demolished in 1968-69.

Facing page: In 1952, Charlie Barlow, farm bailiff of Ickles Hall Farm, was photographed getting in the harvest against a backdrop of Templeborough Melting Shop. The houses at Templeborough, with the prominent Temple Hotel were swept away to allow for the rebuilding of the melting shop during 1960-63. Ickles Hall was demolished by Steel, Peech and Tozer in 1939 but the land contunued to be farmed until it became the site of Brinsworth Strip Mill in 1955-58.

Left: Templeborough Melting shop was erected in 1917 by Steel, Peech and Tozer, with government assistance, to meet the increased demand caused by the War. A quarter of a mile long, it housed 14 80 ton open-hearth furnaces. The two men in the foreground are said to be T. Osborne and Mr. Creehan.

Right: Looking east along the open hearth furnaces at Templeborough. The melting shop was demolished during "Operation Spear" in 1960-63 to allow the installation of the largest electric arc melting shop in the world—six furnaces of around 100 tons capacity. SPEAR was an acronym for Steel Peech Electric Arc Reorganisation.

The transport fleet of Yates and Haywood is lined up for inspection, c. 1920. Horses obviously still had a part to play. The lorries appear to be a Thorneycroft, two Fiats and a Guy. The cone in the background was part of Beatson Clark's glassworks.

A magnetic crane unloads axle blanks from a Sentinel steam lorry onto a Lister diesel truck at Owen and Dyson Ltd. c. 1929. Owen and Dyson specialised in the production of railway wheels. Founded in 1875, the company was incorporated in 1907 with Steel, Peech and Tozer as a major shareholder. It became a wholly-owned subsidiary of the United Steel Cos. in 1955.

3 The people

For over 2 centuries the iron and steel industry has been a major employer of labour within the town of Rotherham. In 1933 the Borough Council was able to claim that the town housed the largest single producer of steel in the country (Steel, Peech and Tozer) with a workforce of 4250 men "even in the depression". By 1961 almost a third of the economically active male population of the borough was employed in the industry, a figure that does not include the workforce at places such as Parkgate. Work on the shop floor in the industry was rarely anything other than hot and hard. Despite this, in the 19th century at least, the workforce had a reputation for industry and sobriety. In 1865 John Guest was able to say of the workforce of Park Gate Iron and Steel Co:-

"It is highly to the credit of the men of Parkgate, that many of them know not only how to earn large wages, but also how to make the best use of what they earn; very many of the them have comfortable dwellinghouses of their own, they have also had for some years a good Temperance Hall, a Wesleyan Chapel, and are now about erecting a Church, and a Methodist Free Church, showing very unmistakably that with material progress, they have the discernment and determination to provide also for that mental, moral and religious advancement, without which a largely increasing community may be anything but a peaceful, prosperous and happy one."

Right: The staff and foreman of the Midland Iron Co., Masbrough, were posed for the photographer in 1887. Among the men pictured here are A. B. Baylis, secretary and manager Charles Norburn, works manager, Robert Whysall, engineer, William Liversedge, chief clerk and T. H. Osborn, representative.

The staff and foremen of the Midland Iron Co., Rotherham, in 1887. When this picture was taken the present Managing Director, Mr. Albert Corker, who was then a mere boy, had gone for his holidays—
to Whiston. At this period Mr. A. B. Baylis was the secretary and manager, Mr. Charles Norburn works manager, Mr. Robert Wigyall engineer, Mr. William Liversidge chief clerk, and Mr. T. H. Osborn
representative.
Names (from left to right)—Back row: Messrs. T. Grayson, James Marsden, George Sheardown, H. G. Liversidge, John Boyes, James Aston, Robert Nelson, James Sansam, George Turner, John
Sorsby, Edward Crossley, Nathaniel Taylor, John Wainwright, Joseph Bruce, E. J. Alvey and Hugh Challener. Seated: Messrs. William Thompson, Francis Davy, Harry Wood, Robert Wigyall, T. H. Osborn,
A. B. Baylis, William Liversidge, Charles Norburn, William Wright and Frank Yeardley.

Above: Four workers in the forge at Steel, Peech and Tozer pose in front of a small steam hammer, c. 1910.

Left: The personnel of Steel, Peech and Tozer's rail mill, photographed in 1903.

Above: Three employees of Steel, Peech and Tozer pose in front of a stack of rolled railway tyres, c. 1920. The size of the tyres would indicate that they were intended for locomotive driving wheels.

Right: A group of workers at Parkgate Iron and Steel Works pose in front of a diminutive shunting locomotive, c. 1905.

Facing page: Another of the Steel, Peech and Tozer groups taken in 1934-35, this photograph shows the personnel of the 10" and 14" mills at Ickles which were directly behind the offices and main gate. In 1961 these mills were under the control of the new appointed works manager (re-rolling mills) Mr. R. Scholey, now better known as Sir Bob Scholey, C.B.E., Chairman of British Steel. The rolling mills were demolished in 1976.

Above: Workers in the Disc Mill at Steel, Peech and Tozer, take a breather in the 1930s.

Right: Members of the Engineers Dept., Steel, Peech and Tozer, photographed c. 1934-35. Most departments in the works seem to have had group photographs taken at that time. The men are identified as follows: back row: A. Mitchell, R. Smith, D. Broadhead, J. Tompkins, —, —, —, —, G. Bilton; middle row, J. Norburn, C. Nicholls, G. Ball, W. Bilton, —, —, —; front row, —, —, —, H. Windle, —, —, —, —.

Below: Workmen at John Baker and Bessemer Ltd. some time in the 1930s. The photograph would appear to have been taken at the Brinsworth Iron and Wheels Works, rather than at the company's Kilnhurst works.

Above:Another 1934-35 photograph, this time of the personnel of the Rotherham Melting Shops which lay on the north side of the River Don. The men are: back row, —, F. Peacock, Reg Butler, H. Kilby, Bill Chambers, Jack Swallow, - Quinton, D. MacDonald, —, George Ellis, A. Budworth, Harold Butcher, Cyril Tomlins; centre row, A. Pendell, B. Cumberlidge, Fred Bell, Eddie Edwards, J. Ryecroft, G. Sawford, B. Archer, J. Morgan; front row, Jack Garner, Bob Thompson, Tom Hardiman, Ginger Roberts, A. Denton, J. Potts, G. Bailey, Bernard Gilbert, Norman Linacre, A. Lee.

During 1976 the electric arc melting shops at Templeborough and Aldwarke consistently broke production records. This photograph shows the record breaking team at Aldwarke. During November the 'N' furnace produced 8,467 tonnes in one week on continuous feeding and the 'K' furnace produced the best ever basket charged performance in BSC history with 7,704 tonnes in one week.

4 Casting iron

For over two centuries the manufacture of stove grates and light, decorative castings was a staple of Rotherham industry. This trade pre-dated the heavy iron and steel industry that later became synonymous with Rotherham, having originated in the mid-18 Century with the Walkers. In the 19th Century the products of Yates Haywood and Co., W. H. Micklethwait and Co., Skelton, Corbitt and Co., George Wright (Rotherham) Ltd. and Hattersley Bros. were sold worldwide. Even Buckingham Palace had Rotherham-made fireplaces. The 20th Century was marked by a steady decline in the industry, particularly after 1945. By 1970 the declining popularity of solid fuel, coupled with undercapitalisation and inefficiency had brought a once prosperous industry to nothing.

Left: A large cooking range (for a hotel or country house) is in the course of erection and in the background can be seen the large diameter driving wheels for the overhead shaft machinery drive.

This photograph is obviously posed; the woman appears to be holding onto a drive belt and the man on the left is grasping a circular saw.

Facing page: Yates, Haywood and Co. was the largest of several ironfounders in Rotherham, specialising in the production of fireplaces, ranges and ornamental ironwork. This photograph and the next two. taken c. 1910, show various sections of the assembly shops at Effingham Works. The appliances shown in this photograph are, left to right, the "KWIXSET" self-acting range, the small "QUEEN" stove and the "3714" gas stove.

Above: A ladle full of molten metal is poured into the casting boxes at J. J. Habershon and Co's. foundry in the 1920s. Habershon's specialised in rolling steel strip but at one time also produced general castings. The gentleman at the left appears to be a member of the offices staff, possibly a metallurgist. He is checking the temperature of the metal with an optical pyrometer.

Right: In this view, in the Old Foundry at Habershon's works in 1926, a billet of red-hot metal is being quenched with water but the purpose of the exercise is uncertain. The gentleman in the bowler hat is Mr. Allison, the workman is F. Guest.

A general view of J. J. Habershon and Son's foundry in the 1920s. The floor is covered in moulders' sand. A line of casting boxes stands ready in front of the furnace. The ladle that can be seen at the left would be filled with molten metal and used to fill the boxes.

Right: A new foundry was built at Habershons in the 1930s. It was a much lighter structure but the floor was still covered in moulder's sand. Large iron casting boxes are here being used to cast new rolls for the company's rolling mills. A modern furnace stands at the left with an older, brick furnace behind it.

5 Making Steel

Steel-making starts with the melting process. Most of the photographs show open hearth furnaces, but electric arc furnaces are now the norm. During the process additional elements may be added to the molten steel, depending on the qualities required in the finished product.

The liquid steel is then 'tapped' or poured into a waiting ladle. The slag or waste products which float on the top is poured off into slag pots. This is allowed to cool and used for road building etc.

The steel is then 'teemed' into waiting ingot moulds which are allowed to cool. The ingot moulds are then 'stripped' off and the ingots put into a reheating furnace to make sure they are of uniform temperature throughout.

The ingots then go through a cogging mill to be rolled into smaller and more manageable sizes (billets, blooms) and go for further rolling into bars of various sizes or steel strips.

Above: A charger deposits its load of scrap or dolomite into an open-hearth furnace at Templeborough, 1949. (Copyright British Steel Corporation, NRRC-157/16/72)

Right: Photographed at Steel, Peech and Tozer in 1949, this charger driver is operating the controls to charge an open-hearth furnace with raw materials. (Copyright British Steel Corporation, NRRC-157/16/72)

Above: The tapping of an open hearth furnace was always a spectacular sight. The crane in the foreground waits to take away the full ladle of molten steel. This photograph was taken in Templeborough Melting Shop in 1961.

Left: These two men are engaged in "fettling" an open-hearth furnace at Templeborough in 1949 and wear the normal protective clothing of the period. Both wear dark glasses against the glare and the one nearest the camera is holding a towel in his mouth as protection against the heat. The "third hand" on the right is Eric Ironmonger. Fettling involves repairing the lining of a furnace using carefully placed shovelsful of refractory material to repair any holes before a new charge of metal is introduced.

Steelmaking has always been a dirty, noisy, dusty and hot occupation but provides endless opportunites for dramatic photographs.
(Copyright British Steel Corporation, NRRC-157/16/72).

Above: Teemer Joe Witham was photographed during the 1950s taking a sample of steel during teeming operations in Templeborough Melting Shop. The man in the trilby is Colin Hawkins. Both Joe Witham and his colleague in the dark glasses are wearing clogs.

Left: Taken in the same place but some 10 to 15 years later, this photograph shows the great change that had taken place in protective head gear. Steel from the electric arc furnaces is being teemed from the ladle into ingot moulds.

74

Facing page: The moulds are here being removed from the now solidified ingots by the 150 ton stripper crane at Templeborough in 1949. The cars then carry the ingots to the soakers, prior to cogging (or initial rolling). (Copyright British Steel Corporation, NRRC-157/16/72).

Left: A 70 cwt. ingot is placed on the rollers of the 42" cogging mill that will reduce it to a 6" slab. (Copyright British Steel Corporation, NRRC-157/16/72).

The hot deseamer removed the small seams or surface cracks that develop during heating and rolling by dressing the surface with oxy-acetylene torches. It is here seen in action at Templeborough in 1949. (Copyright British Steel Corporation, NRRC-157/16/71).

Right: After cogging, the blooms passed to the continuous billet mill which reduced them to the required dimensions. The blooms were automatically cut to length by the bloom shears, here seen in action at Templeborough in 1949.
(Copyright British Steel Corporation, NRRC-157/16/71).

Facing page: A view along the continuous billet mill at Templeborough where four stands of 21" roughing rolls and six stands of 18" finishing rolls reduced the blooms to billets of anything from 5" to $1^1/_2$" square. (Copyright British Steel Corporation, NRRC-157/16/71).

Facing page: A half finished axle bloom is forged in the six-ton hammer shop at Ickles. The workman on the left trips the hammer whilst his colleagues on the right rotate the bloom between blows. The hammer was a product of the Brightside Foundry and Engineering Co. Ltd. of Sheffield.
(Copyright British Steel Corporation, NRRC-157/16/71).

Above: Tapping a blast furnace at Parkgate in the 1960s.

A 60 ton open-hearth furnace is charged with molten iron at Parkgate.

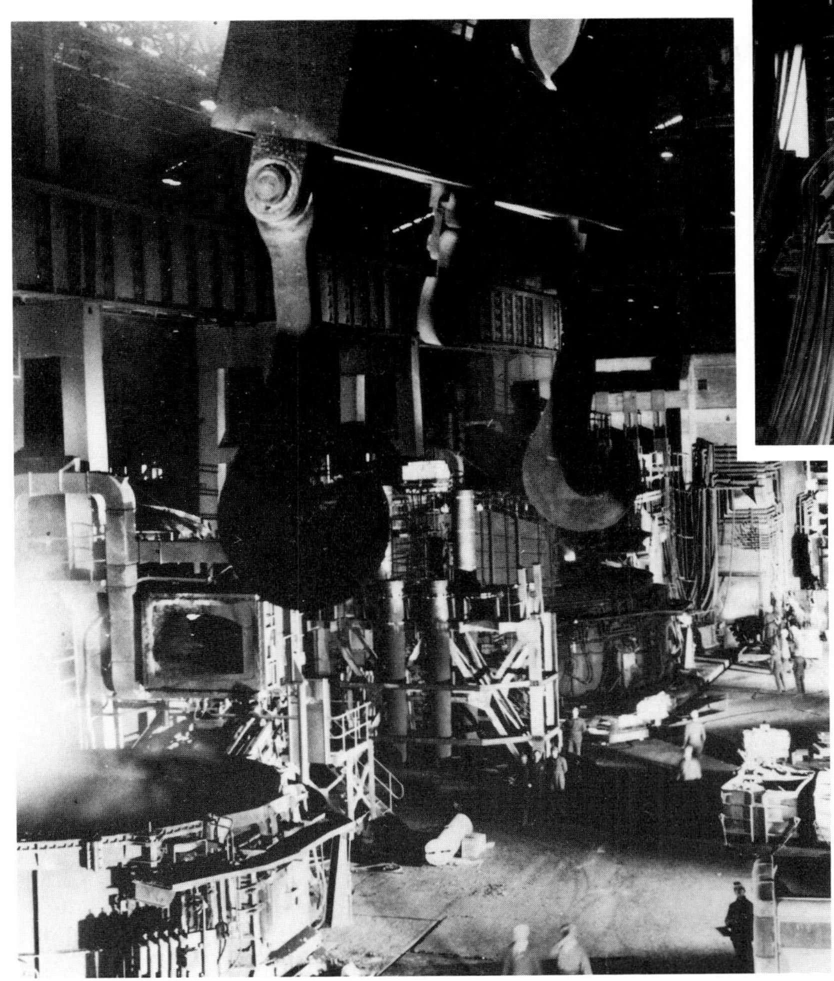

Two views of the electric melting shop at Templeborough, taken in the late 1960s. The 14 open-hearth furnaces were replaced by 6 electric arc furnaces. The furnaces were charged from scrap baskets, one of which is seen in the first photograph.

Facing page: Despite appearances, this is not a NASA command centre, but the control centre for the electric melting shop installed at Templeborough in the 1960s.

Sampling the melt at the electric melting shop, Templeborough, in the 1960s.

This view of the spring shop at Steel, Peech and Tozer probably dates from the 1930s. The heavyweight laminated springs in the foreground would be destined for railway wagons or heavy lorries.

6 Working Steel

Steel once made can be worked in various ways. As well as the rolling processes it can be forged, either under hammers or in large presses, or cast-poured into moulds in a foundry.

The products made from Rotherham iron and steel have always been many and varied. A directory of the 1920s listed dozens of different types of steel and finished products manufactured in the town ranging from agricultural steel, aircraft steels, alloy steels, armature shafts and axles to wagons, water storage tanks, wheels, wire, worm shafts and wrought iron bars.

Many of the photographs in this section show women workers in the steel works in the war years. The Park Gate Iron and Steel Co. started employing women manual workers in April, 1941, and were employing over 700 by the middle of 1943; they were involved in a very wide range of jobs including scrap burning, furnace charging, plate burning, crane driving and labouring. This was not only true of the Second World War; the painting reproduced on the back cover shows women working in Kilnhurst Steelworks in 1918.

The pit arch and prop department at Park Gate Iron and Steel Co. produced roof supports for underground roadways in collieries. In the centre of this photograph, taken in the 1930s, steel girders are being bent to the correct profile. The workman in the foreground is drilling holes in the fishplates that were used to fasten the sections of the arch together.

Facing page: Also dating from the 1930s is this view of the 10" rolling mill at Park Gate. After its initial passage through the bottom pair of rolls in each stand, the red hot steel was grasped with tongs and passed back through the top pair to be further reduced in section. There was a noticeable lack of protective clothing.

This photograph is uncaptioned, but also appears to show the bar straightening machine at Park Gate Iron and Steel Co.

Facing page: In common with many other industries, the steel industry took on many women during the war to do jobs that would earlier have been regarded strictly as "man's work". Captioned as "somewhere in England" this photograph was in fact taken at Park Gate Iron and Steel Co. Unrecognisable under the protective clothing, Mrs. J. Dobson is here flame dressing steel bars.

Right: Even locomotive driving fell to women during the war. Miss M. Hawkins, formerly an assistant in a chemist's shop, is shown at the controls of one of the locomotives at Park Gate Iron and Steel Co. This is one of a series taken to show the part women were playing in vital war production. The locomotive (Hunslet Engine Co., works no. 1981 of 1938) was named after Sir William Bird who became chairman of the company in 1937.

Facing page (bottom): Also taken at Park Gate Iron and Steel Co., Mrs. B. Hague and Mrs. M. Evans (both former housewives) are seen operating a bar straightening machine. The overhead crane driver is Miss F. Gallimore, formerly in domestic service.

A considerable number of women remained in shop floor jobs in the steel industry after the war. In August 1958 Mrs. A. Dowling was the first woman to win an award under Steel, Peech and Tozer's works award scheme. Her suggestion, fixing a file on the welding machines in the Cold Rolling Mill, thus enabling coil ends to be cleaned before welding, won her £3.

We do not know this girl's name as the photograph is uncaptioned. She is operating the trip level on a small hammer while her male colleague manipulates the workpiece.

SODA

These three views illustrate the production of wheels and tyres at John Baker and Bessemer Ltd. in the 1950s. The first photographs shows a railway tyre being rolled to the finished size. Two hydraulic wheel presses can be seen in the second photograph. An ingot awaits forging under the right-hand press while a finished blank is ready for removal on the left. The blanks then passed to the wheel mill to be brought to the correct diameter and thickness. In the third view the workman is gauging the thickness of the blank with calipers.

This general view of the new tyre mill at Ickles dates from the 1970s and shows a large ring in the process of rolling.

Left: A billet is withdrawn from the furnace at the 18" mill at Parkgate in the 1960s.

Another manually operated rolling mill, this time photographed at the Midland Iron Co. in 1944.

In 1952 a Centurion tank was displayed at Steel, Peech and Tozer where several of its components were made. Note the gun barrel and rolled turret rings at the right.

Facing page: Completed sets of wheels and axles await delivery at Owen and Dyson's in the 1960s. Note the double sets of rails that allowed the wheel sets to be interleaved, saving on storage space.
(Copyright British Steel Corporation, NRRC-157/16/71).

7 BEHIND THE SCENES

The men and women who make or work steel are only some of the employees in a large steelworks. There are the maintenance staff, electricians, fitters, engineers, office staff (sales, typing, wages and now computer personnel) the staff of the drawing office and engineering departments, and people working in catering and welfare. Steel, Peech and Tozer even had its own weekly works newspaper and its own internal bus service.

Although some thirty years separate these two photographs, there seems to have been little change in the calculating machines. The earlier view was taken at J. J. Habershon and Sons in the 1930s, the later view at Steel, Peech and Tozer in the 1960s. (Copyright of above, British Steel Corporation, NRCC-157/16/66).

In the days before bank accounts and credit transfer became the rule rather than the exception, pay day involved a great deal of counting of pounds, shillings and pence. Here we see the Wages Dept. of Steel, Peech and Tozer checking that they have enough raw material.
(Copyright British Steel Corporation, NRRC-157/16/66).

This photograph of part of the large typing pool at Steel, Peech and Tozer was probably taken in the early 1960s.

NOTICE

Steel-making is thirsty work. A workman collects his tea can from the works canteen at Steel, Peech and Tozer in the 1960s. There were three works canteens which between them served over 120,000 meals and snacks each month. (Copyright British Steel Corporation, NRRC-157/16/66).

Facing page: The afternoon shift clocks-on at Steel, Peech and Tozer in the 1960s. (Copyright British Steel Corporation, NRRC-157/16/66).

Right: Fire is an ever-present hazard in a steel-works and Steel, Peech and Tozer had its own works fire brigade from an early date. This became doubly important during the Second World War. Some of the war-time fire fighters were photographed with their Coventry Climax pump, next to the River at Ickles.

The Diocese of Sheffield introduced Industrial Missions after the war. The first chaplain at Steel, Peech and Tozer was the aptly named Rev. Scott Paradise, an American. He is here seen holding a meeting in the works, probably with the furnace bricklayers. In the foreground is ladleman Percy Fisher and on the extreme right is senior union official Colin Windle. Rev. Paradise returned to the USA in April 1957 to undertake similar work in Detroit.

8 Sports and social activities

The photographs in this section give a glimpse of the many social and sporting activites that were enjoyed by workers in the industry.

This group of Steel, Peech and Tozer officials and foremen were photographed during an outing to Newark in 1914. They are identified as: standing, rear, Bernard Methley, F. Wood, —, George Dyer; back row, W. Coulson, C. Watson, H. Allen, Sam Wood, Percy Steel (in bowler hat), H. Palethorpe, Fred Watson, E.Palethorpe, Sam Allen, Alf Mitchell, Fred Heath, - Earley, W. Norton, Frank Watson, —, G. Picken, J. Russell; seated, Sam Beecher, G. Ross, J. Russum, B. Graham, G. Powell, A. Deighton, Matthew Allot, Tom Palethorpe, Jack Hunter, J. Tompkins, Sam Allen; on ground, Fred Robinson, Japanese student, Sam Allen, A. Fielding, Bert Douglas. Note that there were three Sam Allens. They worked respectively in the foundry, bricklayers and tyre mill.

This photograph of the Phoenix Brass Band, was probably taken in the Phoenix Hall at Ickles c. 1935. 'Phoenix' was the trade mark of Steel, Peech and Tozer. It derived from the Phoenix Bessemer Steel Co., a small, short-lived steelworks at Ickles which was taken over by Henry Steel and William Peech when they went into partnership in 1875. The brass band was one of the many branches of Phoenix Social Services that included operatic and photographic societies and numerous sports clubs.

Left: Perhaps someone will recognise themselves among this crowd at a Phoenix Social Services dance in the Clifton Hall in January 1960. From 1954 the music at these dances was provided by Victor Sylvester and his Orchestra. By 1959 they were so popular that the dance had to be held over two days.

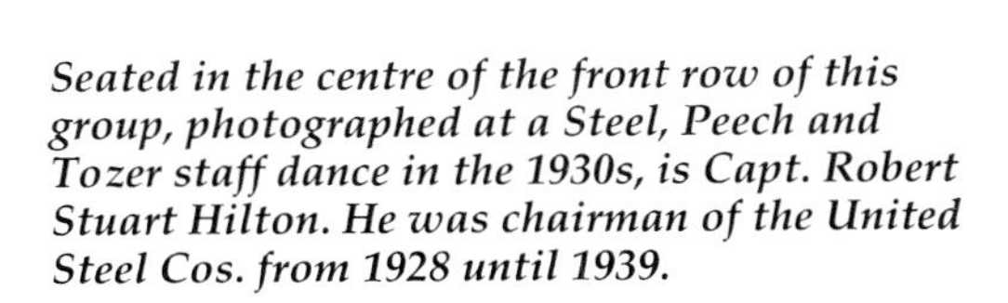

Seated in the centre of the front row of this group, photographed at a Steel, Peech and Tozer staff dance in the 1930s, is Capt. Robert Stuart Hilton. He was chairman of the United Steel Cos. from 1928 until 1939.

The members of the Steel, Peech and Tozer Ladies' Hockey Team, photographed c. 1935, include, back row, G. Tracey, Edith Hollingsworth, S. Allen, F. Marshall, —, —, M. Lomas; front row, R. Rawlins, L. Grey, C. Ray, E. Turner, - Jameson.

There were several Steel, Peech and Tozer football teams playing in local leagues in addition to a thriving inter-departmental competition within the works. The Tyre team are here seen with the Inter-Departmental Trophy which they won in 1953. They went on to represent Steel, Peech and Tozer in the United Steel Cos. competition but were beaten 3-2 in the semi-final by Appleby Frodingham.

Above: Steel, Peech and Tozer was one of the few works in the area to have its own golf course, at Brinsworth. Opened in 1932, the course was extended as and when finances allowed, reaching 14 holes in 1938 and 18 holes in 1952.

Both Steel, Peech and Tozer and Park Gate Iron and Steel Co. held annual galas for employees and families. This tug-of-war was photographed at a Parkgate gala in the early 1970s.

Right: In the years when variety was still alive, a visit to a steelworks seems to have been an essential part of any show business celebrity's appearance in Sheffield or Rotherham. Ronnie Hilton was in the early days of his singing career when he was photographed in the melting shop at Steel, Peech and Tozer during his visit in November 1955.

A very young Benny Hill made his visit to Steel, Peech and Tozer in August 1954. He is seen talking to Bill Cooke and Sid Easthorpe while one of the open-hearth furnaces is tapped in the background.

Victor Sylvester's annual visits have already been mentioned. He is seen here in 1960, outside No. 1 Gate, with members of his band.

9 The future

Most of what is pictured in this book has gone. To the natural change and development which affect all industries have been added a new combination of automation, world recession and the new obliteration of the traditional heavy industries. This has wiped out the old iron and steel industry as we have known it. More than 8,000 jobs have been lost since 1978 and numerous works are gone for good. The Don Valley seems a desolation of empty buildings and derelict sites.

But this picture is too gloomy. It does seem that the contraction of the industry is nearing its end. Regular announcements are now forthcoming of new investents, new plant and new records set in production. The Phoenix, the bird reborn in the flames, may still be an apt symbol for the industry, ensuring that Rotherham will continue to be a major producer within the British Steel Industry and that, computerised and automated, there is still plenty of life in steel.

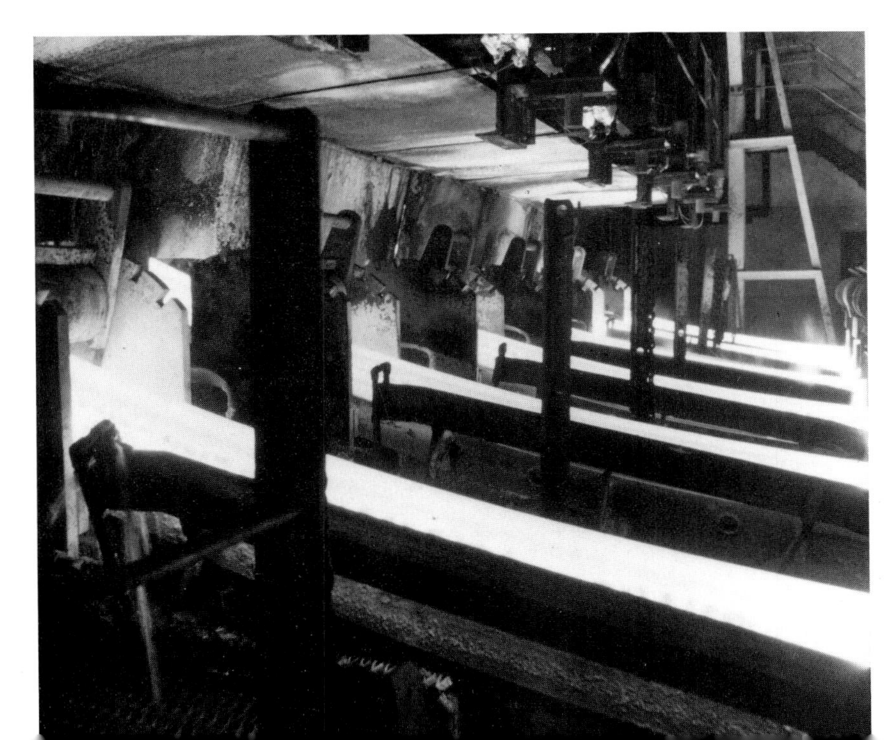

Concasting at Templeborough.